ight, What so proud-ly we hail'd at the twi-light's last
leep, Where the foe's haugh-ty host in dread si - lence re-
wore, That the hav - oc of war and the bat-tle's con-
stand Be - tween their loved homes and the war's des - o-

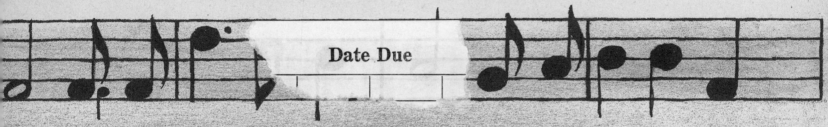

fight, O'er the ram-parts we watch'd were so gal - lant - ly
steep As it fit - ful -ly blows, half con-ceals, half dis-
more? Their blood has wash'd out their foul foot-step's pol-
land Praise the Power that hath made and pre-served us a

ir, Gave proof thro' the night that our flag was still there.
eam, In full glo - ry re-flect-ed now__ shines in the stream.
ve From the ter-ror of flight or the gloom of the grave;
ist, And this be our mot - to, "In God is our trust."

wave__O'er the land_ of the free and the home of the brave?
wave__O'er the land_ of the free and the home of the brave.
wave__O'er the land_ of the free and the home of the brave.
wave__O'er the land_ of the free and the home of the brave.

THE
STAR SPANGLED BANNER

☆

Written by FRANCIS SCOTT KEY
during the attack on Fort McHenry,
September 13 and 14, 1814

The Star Spangled Banner

Pictured by **Ingri & Edgar Parin d'Aulaire**

DOUBLEDAY & COMPANY, INC., GARDEN CITY, NEW YORK

The drawings for this book were lithographed directly on stone by the artists
and the book was printed in five colors by George C. Miller, New York,
in the United States of America

Oh, say, can you see,

by the dawn's early light,

What so proudly we hailed

at the twilight's last gleaming?

Whose broad stripes
and bright stars,
through the perilous fight,
o'er the ramparts we watched
were so gallantly streaming?

And the rocket's red glare,
the bombs bursting in air,
Gave proof through the night
that our flag was still there.

Oh, say, does that Star Spangled Banner yet wave

O'er the land of the free and the home of the brave?

On the shore dimly seen

through the mists of the deep,

Where the foe's haughty host

in dread silence reposes,

What is that which the breeze,
o'er the towering steep
As it fitfully blows,
half conceals, half discloses?

Now it catches the gleam
of the morning's first beam,
In full glory reflected
now shines in the stream,

'Tis the Star Spangled Banner, O long may it wave

O'er the land of the free and the home of the brave.

And where is the band

who so vauntingly swore,

That the havoc of war

and the battle's confusion,

A home and a country

should leave us no more?

Their blood has washed out

their foul footstep's pollution.

No refuge could save

the hireling and slave

From the terror of flight

or the gloom of the grave;

And the Star Spangled Banner, in triumph doth wave

O'er the land of the free and the home of the brave.

Oh thus be it ever

when freemen shall stand

Between their loved homes

and the war's desolation.

Blessed with victory and peace,
may the heaven rescued land

Praise the Power

that hath made

and preserved us a nation!

Then conquer we must,

when our cause it is just,

And this be our motto,

"In God is our trust."

And the Star Spangled Banner, in triumph shall wave

O'er the land of the free and the home of the brave.

Oh,___ say, can you see, by the dawn's ear - ly
On the shore dim - ly seen thro' the mists of the
And___where is the band who so vaunt-ing - ly
Oh___ thus be it ev - er when free-men shall

gleam-ing? Whose broad stripes and bright stars, thro' the per - il-ous
pos - es, What is that which the breeze, o'er the tow-er-ing
fu - sion A____ home and a coun - try should leave us no
la - tion. Blest with vict' - ry and peace, may the heav'n res-cued

stream-ing? And the rock-et's red glare, the bombs burst - ing in
clos - es? Now it catch-es the gleam of the morn-ing's first
lu - tion. No ref - uge could save the ___ hire - ling and
na - tion! Then con-quer we must, when our cause it is

Oh, say, does that___ Star Span-gled Ban - ner___ yet
'T is the Star-Span-gled___ Ban - ner, O long - may___ it ___
And the Star-Span-gled___ Ban - ner, in tri - umph___ doth___
And the Star-Span-gled___ Ban - ner, in tri - umph shall___